Student Success Toolbox

Improving Learning and Performance through Assessment

Pre-Market Edition

published by

Pacific Crest
Lisle, IL

Student Success Toolbox

Improving Learning and Performance through Assessment

Pre-Market Edition

Layout, Production, and Cover Design by Denna Hintze-Yates

Copyright © 2009

Pacific Crest
906 Lacey Avenue, Suite 206
Lisle, IL 60532
800-421-9826
www.pcrest.com

ISBN: 978-1-60263-110-6

Table of Contents

*While this book will work well on
its own, the companion web site:*

www.**studentsuccesstoolbox**.com

*provides access to additional tools, blank
forms, rubrics, methodologies, and more!*

General Tools

Log of Entries

Glossary

Concept Map Form

Addressing & Avoiding Errors

Reading Log

Learning Journal

Feel free to use this page for notes!

Name	_____		**Log of**
Course	_____		**Entries**
Semester/Term	_____		

Date	Page	Activity	Summary of Entry

Date	Page	Activity	Summary of Entry

Transfer new vocabulary words, specialized phrases, formulas, and important calculations to this section.

Glossary

Word or Term

Definition, proper use, explanation, source, and page

A-B

C-D

Word or Term	Definition, proper use, explanation, source, and page
E-G	
H-K	

Word or Term   **Definition, proper use, explanation, source, and page**

L-M

_____   _____
_____   _____
_____   _____
_____   _____
_____   _____
_____   _____
_____   _____
_____   _____
_____   _____
_____   _____
_____   _____
_____   _____
_____   _____
_____   _____
_____   _____
_____   _____

N-P

_____   _____
_____   _____
_____   _____
_____   _____
_____   _____
_____   _____
_____   _____
_____   _____
_____   _____
_____   _____
_____   _____
_____   _____
_____   _____
_____   _____
_____   _____
_____   _____
_____   _____

Word or Term

Q-S

Definition, proper use, explanation, source, and page

_____ _____
_____ _____
_____ _____
_____ _____
_____ _____
_____ _____
_____ _____
_____ _____
_____ _____
_____ _____
_____ _____
_____ _____
_____ _____
_____ _____
_____ _____
_____ _____

T-V

_____ _____
_____ _____
_____ _____
_____ _____
_____ _____
_____ _____
_____ _____
_____ _____
_____ _____
_____ _____
_____ _____
_____ _____
_____ _____
_____ _____

Word or Term	Definition, proper use, explanation, source, and page
W-Z	
Numerical	

Formula or Key Idea	Definition, proper use, explanation, source, and page

Concept Map Form

Name or Team Members:

Concept

Associated Concepts

Sample Concept Map of "Concept Maps"

Concept maps are graphical tools for organizing and representing knowledge. They include concepts, usually enclosed in circles or boxes of some type, and relationships between concepts indicated by a connecting line linking two concepts. Words on the line, referred to as linking words or linking phrases, specify the relationship between the two concepts. (From: Novak, J. D. & A. J. Cañas, The Theory Underlying Concept Maps and How to Construct Them, Technical Report IHMC CmapTools 2006-01 Rev 01-2008, Florida Institute for Human and Machine Cognition, 2008", available at: http://cmap.ihmc.us/Publications/ResearchPapers/TheoryUnderlyingConceptMaps.pdf.)

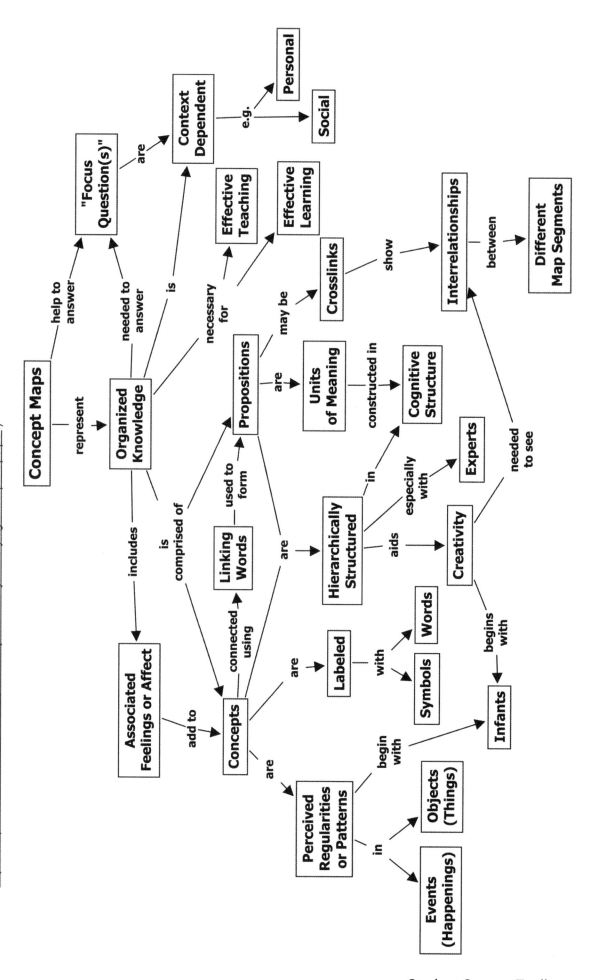

Name _____

Focus or Course _____

OOPS! Addressing & Avoiding Errors

Error description examples: Misapplication of a Rule, Incorrect Assumption, Failure to Follow Instructions, Lack of Understanding, etc.

Error Description (What kind of error is this?)	Example of Error (demonstrate the error; use a diagram/drawing if needed)	Context where error occurs (When do you make this error?)

Reason for error (Why do you make this error?)	Correct Procedure (correction of example shown above)	How I will avoid making this error in the future

Error Description (What kind of error is this?)	Example of Error (demonstrate the error; use a diagram/drawing if needed)	Context where error occurs (When do you make this error?)

Reason for error (Why do you make this error?)	Correct Procedure (correction of example shown above)	How I will avoid making this error in the future

Name _____

Focus or Course _____

Addressing & Avoiding Errors

Error description examples: Misapplication of a Rule, Incorrect Assumption, Failure to Follow Instructions, Lack of Understanding, etc.

Error Description (What kind of error is this?)	Example of Error (demonstrate the error; use a diagram/drawing if needed)	Context where error occurs (When do you make this error?)

Reason for error (Why do you make this error?)	Correct Procedure (correction of example shown above)	How I will avoid making this error in the future

Error Description (What kind of error is this?)	Example of Error (demonstrate the error; use a diagram/drawing if needed)	Context where error occurs (When do you make this error?)

Reason for error (Why do you make this error?)	Correct Procedure (correction of example shown above)	How I will avoid making this error in the future

Name _____

Focus or Course _____

Addressing & Avoiding Errors

Error description examples: Misapplication of a Rule, Incorrect Assumption, Failure to Follow Instructions, Lack of Understanding, etc.

Error Description (What kind of error is this?)	**Example of Error** (demonstrate the error; use a diagram/drawing if needed)	**Context where error occurs** (When do you make this error?)
Reason for error (Why do you make this error?)	**Correct Procedure** (correction of example shown above)	**How I will avoid making this error in the future**

Error Description (What kind of error is this?)	**Example of Error** (demonstrate the error; use a diagram/drawing if needed)	**Context where error occurs** (When do you make this error?)
Reason for error (Why do you make this error?)	**Correct Procedure** (correction of example shown above)	**How I will avoid making this error in the future**

Focus or Course _____

samples

Addressing & Avoiding Errors
OOPS!

Error description examples: Misapplication of a Rule, Incorrect Assumption, Failure to Follow Instructions, Lack of Understanding, etc.

Error Description (What kind of error is this?)	Example of Error (demonstrate the error; use a diagram/drawing if needed)	Context where error occurs (When do you make this error?)
Using an apostrophe for the possessive of "it" Misapplication of a Rule	The cat ate (it's) food.	I make this error each time I use the possessive form of "it".

Reason for error (Why do you make this error?)	Correct Procedure (correction of example shown above)	How I will avoid making this error in the future
I don't distinguish between "it" possessive (belonging to) and the contraction of "it is"	The cat ate its food.	ANY time I write "its" I will think, "Use an apostrophe ONLY if I mean IT IS."

Error Description (What kind of error is this?)	Example of Error (demonstrate the error; use a diagram/drawing if needed)	Context where error occurs (When do you make this error?)
Not placing the decimal correctly in the answer to a decimal calculation. Calculation Error	The decimal point is in the wrong position in the answer. I should have counted 4 places from the right-most digit. $\begin{array}{r} \overset{1}{}\overset{1}{} \\ 0.312 \\ \times\ 1.5 \\ \hline 1560 \\ 03120 \\ \hline .04680 \end{array}$	I tend to make this error when there is a leading or ending zero in ANY of the numbers (factors OR their product).

Reason for error (Why do you make this error?)	Correct Procedure (correction of example shown above)	How I will avoid making this error in the future
I do not carefully count the decimal places in the factors so that I can place it correctly in their product.	$\begin{array}{r} \overset{1}{}\overset{1}{} \\ 0.312 \\ \times\ 1.5 \\ \hline 1560 \\ 03120 \\ \hline 0.4680 \end{array}$ 4 places	I'll review my work, counting decimal places in problems, writing down that number. Then I'll draw arrows showing the decimal moving, place by place, for EVERY problem until carefully counting places becomes a habit.

Student Success Toolbox

Name _____

Book/Title _____

Reading Log

Pages _____

Date _____

1 Purpose of Reading

My objectives are:

My performance criteria are:

Minutes I expect to spend reading: _____

2 First Reading (skim)

Notes and observations (identify at least three major points):

3 Key Vocabulary

Use each key word in a new context or phrase.

_____   _____

_____   _____

_____   _____

_____   _____

4 Outline of Reading key points and flow of content

5 Key Questions to be answered

continued on other side

Second Reading

Two additional inquiry questions that I have for further exploration:

1. _____

2. _____

Summarize

The most important points of the reading were:

Integrate

The relationship between the content of the reading and my previous knowledge and experience is:

Reflect

Actual time (minutes) spent reading: _____

The following affected (positively or negatively) the quality of my reading performance:

Instructor Feedback

Strengths:

Areas for Improvement:

Insights:

Name _____

Book/Title

Reading Log

Pages _____

Date _____

1 Purpose of Reading

My objectives are:

4 Outline of Reading key points and flow of content

My performance criteria are:

5 Key Questions to be answered

Minutes I expect to spend reading: _____

2 First Reading (skim)

Notes and observations (identify at least three major points):

3 Key Vocabulary   Use each key word in a new context or phrase.

_____   _____

_____   _____

_____   _____

_____   _____

continued on other side

6 Second Reading

Two additional inquiry questions that I have for further exploration:

1. _____

2. _____

7 Summarize

The most important points of the reading were:

8 Integrate

The relationship between the content of the reading and my previous knowledge and experience is:

9 Reflect

Actual time (minutes) spent reading: _____

The following affected (positively or negatively) the quality of my reading performance:

Instructor Feedback

Strengths:

Areas for Improvement:

Insights:

Reading Log

Name __Paula__

Book/Title __The Top Medical Breakthroughs of 2007" Prevention: Jan 2008: 162-169.__

Pages __7 short pages__

Date __April 12__

1 Purpose of Reading

My objectives are:

To see what medical information is being disseminated through popular sources, like Prevention magazine.

To take a break from some of the more serious reading I'm doing in my other classes. I also wanted to see if there were any breakthroughs I hadn't heard of yet.

To practice reading efficiently.

My performance criteria are:

Basic knowledge of the medical breakthroughs, enough to discuss them superficially, at least.

Minutes I expect to spend reading: __20 minutes__

2 First Reading (skim)

Notes and observations (identify at least three major points):

This magazine is written primarily for women, and the breakthroughs highlighted focus on women in the "sandwich" generation, between children and aging parents.

Lots of promises, but little specific research or timetables.

3 Key Vocabulary

Use each key word in a new context or phrase.

__preemptive__ — __Preemptive changes in diet can prevent some diseases.__

__anticoagulant__ — __Aspirin is a common anticoagulant.__

4 Outline of Reading key points and flow of content

The article outlines "medical breakthroughs" of 2007, mainly in the areas of cancer, osteoarthritis, and strokes. Many of the "breakthroughs" should now be standard procedure with a thorough medical check up. The underlying message seems to be that we should all be advocates for our own health, especially women in the "sandwich" generation, who tend to ignore their own health.

5 Key Questions to be answered

What are considered medical breakthroughs?

How do some people get their medical information?

Is there anything I'd like to look into more deeply?

continued on other side

Second Reading

Two additional inquiry questions that I have for further exploration:

1. How much does this kind of article influence people's own health awareness?

2. How many of these "breakthroughs" were made for the sake of profitability?

Summarize

The most important points of the reading were:

There seem to be genuinely new preventative tests and treatments for certain cancers, osteoarthritis, and stroke patients.

Each section of the article (10 in all) gave a short but fairly comprehensive introduction to a specific breakthrough, the way it was discovered, and the promise it holds. Links to additional information for many of the discoveries were available from the online version of the article.

Integrate

The relationship between the content of the reading and my previous knowledge and experience is:

I'd like to do a researched essay on how people get their medical information and whether or not this makes them more vocal advocates for their own health care. I suspect that many people are afraid of knowing too much about their health...there is an attitude of "maybe if I ignore it, it will just go away" that bothers me. But at the same time, *Prevention* is a popular magazine and there is an increasing amount of health information available on many reputable (not to mention questionable) web sites. I would like to try to reconcile those two facts through some research.

Reflect

Actual time (minutes) spent reading: About 25 min

The following affected (positively or negatively) the quality of my reading performance:

Because of the format of several small sections, I skimmed the piece quickly. I did go back to read a few sections more carefully, but the article was not challenging enough to engage me very deeply.

Instructor Feedback	Strengths:
	Areas for Improvement:
	Insights:

Learning Journal

What I learned:	What triggered the learning?
How do I know I've learned it? (validate your learning)	**Why is it important?**
How will I apply my new knowledge *now*?	**How can I apply my learning in the future?**

Name _____

Focus or Course _____

Learning Journal

What I learned:	What triggered the learning?
How do I know I've learned it? (validate your learning)	**Why is it important?**
How will I apply my new knowledge now?	**How can I apply my learning in the future?**

Name _____

Focus or Course _____

Learning Journal

What I learned:	What triggered the learning?
How do I know I've learned it? (validate your learning)	**Why is it important?**
How will I apply my new knowledge *now*?	**How can I apply my learning in the future?**

Learning Journal

What I learned:

I learned how to calculate gas mileage in miles driven per gallon of gas (Miles Per Gallon: MPG).

What triggered the learning?

This was part of the current chapter in my math textbook; the context is multiplication and division of whole numbers.

How do I know I've learned it? (validate your learning)

I have worked the practice problems in the math book and arrived at correct answers. In the world outside my math book, I was able to validate the Miles per Gallon for my car. I looked up the MPG for my make and model car (an average of 26 miles per gallon) and I filled the tank and drove 416 miles on that tank of gas. Doing the division, my gas tank should hold 16 gallons. I looked it up in my owner's manual and it does!

Why is it important?

Being able to calculate how many miles I can drive on a given amount of gas will come in very handy, since I live on a budget. I was thinking of trading in my car for another to save money on gas but I see that I already get more miles per gallon than I would in the car I was thinking of buying. I also know that one of the signs that something is wrong with a car is when the gas mileage drops. If I keep a record of my MPG, this will help me keep my car running well. That's important because I depend on my car.

How will I apply my new knowledge *now*?

I will continue to practice working these problems in anticipation of the upcoming math test.

How can I apply my learning in the future?

I will be able to apply this learning when I need to budget for fuel, whether in my normal driving or for something like a road trip. I will be able to calculate how much it will cost me to drive a given number of miles, because if I know how far I drive, through figuring out how many gallons that takes, I can multiply the cost of gas (per gallon) to find out how much it will cost to drive that distance.

Team Tools

Forming Teams

Because cooperative learning and functioning within teams is a key component of many courses, it is important to become familiar with both the consideration of various roles when designing teams as well as the performance criteria of the respective roles.

The typical workplace has become much more team-oriented over the past two decades, underlining the importance of students learning to work well in teams. Students who participate in team environments are much better prepared to succeed both in further education, as well as on the job, than are those without teaming experience. Although it is not yet common for business or industry to employ formal process-oriented roles for team members, graduates who have used roles frequently in undergraduate courses realize that the use of roles would dramatically improve team performance.

Why Roles are Important

- Using roles helps team members to become interdependent and to be individually accountable for team success

- It helps students increase their learning skills, and speed up the four stages of team development: forming (goal setting), storming (conflict resolution), norming (problem-solving), and performing

- Roles should be rotated frequently so that each student has the opportunity to practice each role and to realize that effective learning requires that teams use a variety of roles simultaneously. Rotating roles discourages dominance by one person and gives all students opportunities to practice social, communication, and leadership skills.

Captain

1. Facilitate the team process, keeping it enjoyable and rewarding for all team members.

2. Make sure each member has a role and is performing within that role.

3. Ensure that all team members can articulate and apply what has been learned.

4. Manage time, stress, and conflict.

5. Accept accountability for the overall performance of the team.

6. Contribute to the group as an active learner.

Recorder

1. Record group roles and instructions at the beginning of a task or activity.

2. During an activity, record and collect important information and data, integrating and synthesizing different points of view.

3. Document group decisions and discoveries legibly and accurately.

4. Accept accountability for the overall quality of the Recorder's Report.

5. Control information flow and articulate concepts in alternative forms if necessary.

6. Contribute to the group as an active learner.

Spokesperson

1. Speak for the team when called upon to do so.

2. Ask questions or request clarification for the team.

3. Make oral presentations to the class for the team.

4. Use the Recorder's journal to share the team's discoveries and insights.

5. Collaborate periodically with the Recorder.

6. Contribute to the group as an active learner.

Technology Specialist

1. Use the available technological tools for the team activity.

2. Listen, converse, and collaborate with team members; synthesize inputs, try suggestions and/or follow directions for the technology.

3. Retrieve information from various sources; manage the available resources and information.

4. Help team members understand the technology and its use.

5. Be willing to experiment, take risks, and try things.

6. Contribute to the group as an active learner.

Planner

1. Review the activity, develop a plan of action, and revise the plan to ensure task completion.

2. Monitor the team's performance against the plan and report deviations.

3. Contribute to the group as an active learner.

Reflector

1. Assess performance, interactions, and the dynamics among team members, recording strengths, improvements, and insights.

2. Be a good listener and observer.

3. Accept accountability for the overall quality of the Reflector's journal.

4. Present an oral Reflector's Report positively and constructively if asked to do so.

5. Intervene with suggestions and strategies for improving the team's processes.

6. Contribute to the group as an active learner.

Optimist

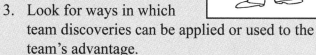

1. Focus on why things will work.

2. Keep the team in a positive frame of mind.

3. Look for ways in which team discoveries can be applied or used to the team's advantage.

4. Contribute to the group as an active learner.

Timekeeper

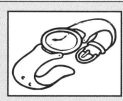

1. Observe the time resource for the activity and/or record the time allocation announced by the facilitator.

2. Keep track of the elapsed time for various tasks and notify the Captain when the agreed-upon time has expired.

3. Contribute to the group as an active learner.

Skeptic

1. Question and check the assumptions that are being made.

2. Determine the issues or reasons why quality is not being met at the expected level.

3. Be constructive in helping the team improve performance.

4. Contribute to the group as an active learner.

Conflict Resolver

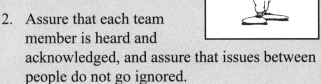

1. Make sure that team members are respectful to each other.

2. Assure that each team member is heard and acknowledged, and assure that issues between people do not go ignored.

3. Check that decisions made by the team are consistent with the team's desired outcomes.

4. Contribute to the group as an active learner.

Spy

1. Eavesdrop on other teams during an activity to gather information and seek clarification or direction.

2. Relay information that can help the team perform better.

3. Contribute to the group as an active learner.

Performance Criteria for Team Roles

A Written Reflector's Report should

- be concise
- be clear
- be accurate
- cite specific examples to convey meaning
- refer to key skills used by the team
- provide supporting documentation
- document affective/emotional issues
- prioritize the most important information
- focus on areas identified in the performance criteria

An Oral Reflector's Report should

- be delivered loudly and clearly enough for all others to hear
- present information concisely (within about 30 seconds, unless specified otherwise)
- identify one strength of the team's performance and explain why it is a strength
- identify one area for improvement that the team can focus on and explain how the improvement can be made
- provide one insight gained about the learning process and explain the significance of the insight

A Written Recorder's Report should

- record accurate information
- identify the team's most important discoveries
- summarize the processes used by the team and identify the context
- identify the concepts and tools used by the team

Name _____

Team _____

Date _____ Time Allotted _____

Meeting/Activity _____

Planner's Report

Planning

Outcomes *(what should the meeting/activity accomplish?)*

_____

_____

Resources Required *(tools, handouts, technology, etc.)*

_____

_____

Preparation Required *(what should team members do to prepare for the meeting/activity?)*

_____

_____

Personnel *(if no official team role, indicate "guest")*

Name:	Team Role:
Name:	Team Role:
Name:	Team Role:
Name:	Team Role:
Name:	Team Role:
Name:	Team Role:

Proposed Agenda/Schedule *(what will be the content or focus of the meeting/activity?)*

Achieve closure of previous items:

_____

_____

_____

New items:

_____

_____

_____

Action items (tasks to be accomplished)

_____

_____

_____

continued on other side

Follow-up

Action Item Assignments

Item: _____ Name: _____

Quality expectations: _____

Item: _____ Name: _____

Quality expectations: _____

Item: _____ Name: _____

Quality expectations: _____

Item: _____ Name: _____

Quality expectations: _____

Item: _____ Name: _____

Quality expectations: _____

Item: _____ Name: _____

Quality expectations: _____

Assessment of Meeting/Activity Outcomes

To what degree were outcomes met? (Note strengths and areas for improvement.) _____

_____

_____

To what degree were resources used effectively? (Note strengths and areas for improvement.) _____

_____

_____

To what degree were team members prepared? (Note strengths and areas for improvement.) _____

_____

_____

To what degree was time used effectively? (Note strengths and areas for improvement.) _____

_____

_____

Instructor Feedback

Strengths:

Areas for Improvement:

Insights:

Name _____   **Planner's**
Team _____   **Report**
Date _____ Time Allotted _____
Meeting/Activity _____

Planning

Outcomes *(what should the meeting/activity accomplish?)*

_____

_____

Resources Required *(tools, handouts, technology, etc.)*

_____

_____

Preparation Required *(what should team members do to prepare for the meeting/activity?)*

_____

_____

Personnel *(if no official team role, indicate "guest")*

Name: _____   Team Role: _____

Name: _____   Team Role: _____

Name: _____   Team Role: _____

Name: _____   Team Role: _____

Name: _____   Team Role: _____

Name: _____   Team Role: _____

Proposed Agenda/Schedule *(what will be the content or focus of the meeting/activity?)*

Achieve closure of previous items:

_____

_____

_____

New items:

_____

_____

_____

Action items (tasks to be accomplished)

_____

_____

_____

continued on other side

Follow-up

Action Item Assignments

Item: _____ Name: _____

Quality expectations: _____

Item: _____ Name: _____

Quality expectations: _____

Item: _____ Name: _____

Quality expectations: _____

Item: _____ Name: _____

Quality expectations: _____

Item: _____ Name: _____

Quality expectations: _____

Item: _____ Name: _____

Quality expectations: _____

Assessment of Meeting/Activity Outcomes

To what degree were outcomes met? (Note strengths and areas for improvement.) _____

_____

_____

To what degree were resources used effectively? (Note strengths and areas for improvement.) _____

_____

_____

To what degree were team members prepared? (Note strengths and areas for improvement.) _____

_____

_____

To what degree was time used effectively? (Note strengths and areas for improvement.) _____

_____

_____

Instructor Feedback

Strengths:

Areas for Improvement:

Insights:

Name __Shawna__

Team __The Wanna Be's__

Date __Nov. 17__   Time Allotted __1 hr__

Planner's Report

Meeting/Activity __Planning our team presentation on "Team Roles"__

Planning

Outcomes *(what should the meeting/activity accomplish?)*

We need to come to agreement on the final preparation/details of our presentation.

Resources Required *(tools, handouts, technology, etc.)*

laptop with internet connection, team role write-ups, Student Success Toolbox (book)

Preparation Required *(what should team members do to prepare for the meeting/activity?)*

Team members should review the notes from the last meeting & the criteria for the presentations

Personnel *(if no official team role, indicate "guest")*

Name: __Shawna__   Team Role: __Captain__

Name: __Robert__   Team Role: __Recorder__

Name: __Tilly__   Team Role: __Reflector__

Name: __Blaise__   Team Role: __Spokesperson__

Name: __Jeremy__   Team Role: __Technology Specialist__

Name: _____   Team Role: _____

Proposed Agenda/Schedule *(what will be the content or focus of the meeting/activity?)*

Achieve closure of previous items:

Make sure that everyone has completed their team role write-ups and can share a copy with everyone in the group. Verify with Jeremy that the classroom will support the technology we'll use in our presentation.

New items:

Need to decide when to meet to practice our presentation

Need to decide whether or not to have each person script narration for their part of the presentation

Action items (tasks to be accomplished)

Set a meeting date/time/place for presentation practice

Assign who brings what for the presentation

Assign script write-ups, if we use individual ones

continued on other side

Follow-up

Action Item Assignments

Item: Test wireless connection in classroom   Name: Jeremy

Quality expectations: Need to know *for sure* that internet will be available.

Item: Combine individual role write-ups into a script   Name: Blaise

Quality expectations: All role write-ups should be included and a copy e-mailed to Shawna

Item: E-mail reminder of presentation practice   Name: Robert

Quality expectations: E-mail everyone 3 days before practice session to remind them of time/place

Item: Computer prep & setup   Name: Tilly & Jeremy

Quality expectations: Set up equipment for practice session. Also for final presentation.

Item: Time role write-ups with computer slideshow   Name: Shawna

Quality expectations: Edit script to fit with the slideshow. Bring to practice session; copies for all.

Item: _____   Name: _____

Quality expectations: _____

Assessment of Meeting/Activity Outcomes

To what degree were outcomes met? (Note strengths and areas for improvement.) We were able to decide what tasks we still had to accomplish & assigned them. Anticipate possible decisions before meetings so consensus decision-making is done more quickly; it took a long time for us to discuss & decide when/where to meet.

To what degree were resources used effectively? (Note strengths and areas for improvement.) We used the laptop effectively, allowing everyone the chance to see the final visual presentation. Everyone was helped by having their Student Success Toolbox book for roles. No areas for improvement this time.

To what degree were team members prepared? (Note strengths and areas for improvement.) Everyone had completed their team role write-ups! Yay!! Everyone needed broader preparation – quickly review what others were working on – it would have sped up our review of each other's work.

To what degree was time used effectively? (Note strengths and areas for improvement.) The captain facilitated the review and discussion effectively. Need to start on time – start up a late fee of $1 that will be applied to our team pizza party.

Instructor Feedback

Strengths:

Areas for Improvement:

Insights:

Reflector's Report

Name _____

Team _____

Date _____

Activity _____

1 Team Performance

Our team's greatest strength and why: _____

_____

_____

_____

Our team's greatest area for improvement and how the improvement can be made: _____

_____

_____

_____

An insight gained about learning during this activity: _____

_____

_____

2 Individual Performance

Name: _____ Team Role: _____

Strength: _____

Area for Improvement: _____

Name: _____ Team Role: _____

Strength: _____

Area for Improvement: _____

Name: _____ Team Role: _____

Strength: _____

Area for Improvement: _____

Name: _____ Team Role: _____

Strength: _____

Area for Improvement: _____

Instructor Feedback	Strengths:
	Areas for Improvement:
	Insights:

Reflector's Report

Name _____

Team _____

Date _____

Activity _____

1 Team Performance

Our team's greatest strength and why: _____

_____

_____

_____

Our team's greatest area for improvement and how the improvement can be made: _____

_____

_____

_____

An insight gained about learning during this activity: _____

_____

_____

2 Individual Performance

Name: _____ Team Role: _____

Strength: _____

Area for Improvement: _____

Name: _____ Team Role: _____

Strength: _____

Area for Improvement: _____

Name: _____ Team Role: _____

Strength: _____

Area for Improvement: _____

Name: _____ Team Role: _____

Strength: _____

Area for Improvement: _____

Instructor Feedback

Strengths:

Areas for Improvement:

Insights:

Name _____

Team _____

Date _____

Activity _____

Reflector's Report

1 Team Performance

Our team's greatest strength and why: _____

_____

_____

_____

Our team's greatest area for improvement and how the improvement can be made: _____

_____

_____

_____

An insight gained about learning during this activity: _____

_____

_____

2 Individual Performance

Name: _____ Team Role: _____

Strength: _____

Area for Improvement: _____

Name: _____ Team Role: _____

Strength: _____

Area for Improvement: _____

Name: _____ Team Role: _____

Strength: _____

Area for Improvement: _____

Name: _____ Team Role: _____

Strength: _____

Area for Improvement: _____

Instructor Feedback	Strengths:
	Areas for Improvement:
	Insights:

Name   Sandra

Team   Sandra, Ken, Fred, Sam

Date   4/15

Activity   Team Roles Presentation

Reflector's Report

Team Performance

Our team's greatest strength and why: <u>We were able to overcome our obstacles. People on the team were great about stepping in when there was an obvious need.</u>

Our team's greatest area for improvement and how the improvement can be made: <u>Use Perception Checking more frequently - our team realized that our planning was limited to assigning roles, prepared our presentation without feedback, and used limited communication about the presentation. The instructor assessment feedback helped significantly so we will ask for feedback sooner.</u>

An insight gained about learning during this activity: <u>Going down blind alleys but then listening and making changes is how we improve. You have to try something before you can get feedback.</u>

Individual Performance

Name: <u>Sam</u>   Team Role: <u>Captain</u>

Strength: <u>Is very sensitive to people feeling appreciated and part of the team</u>

Area for Improvement: <u>Slow down when details need to be grasped by everyone.</u>

Name: <u>Jennifer</u>   Team Role: <u>Spokesperson</u>

Strength: <u>Knows how to hold an audience's interest with voice and gestures</u>

Area for Improvement: <u>Produce messages for a specific time period (be aware of time).</u>

Name: <u>Ken</u>   Team Role: <u>Recorder</u>

Strength: <u>Has a lot of experience he is willing to share to help the team</u>

Area for Improvement: <u>Be more assertive in contributing to the team learning.</u>

Name: <u>Sandra</u>   Team Role: <u>Reflector</u>

Strength: <u>Troubleshooting — figuring out what isn't working</u>

Area for Improvement: <u>Intervene on team process at least three times per activity.</u>

Instructor Feedback

Strengths:

Areas for Improvement:

Insights:

Name _____

Team _____

Date _____

Activity _____

Recorder's Report

1 *Before the activity*

Record the basic agenda or plan as outlined by the team leader: _____

_____

_____

_____

_____

_____

_____

2 *During the activity*

Important information to be documented: _____

_____

_____

_____

_____

_____

_____

_____

_____

_____

_____

_____

_____

_____

_____

_____

_____

_____

_____

continued on other side

During the activity

Important information to be referenced. Where did you get key information? _____

_____

_____

_____

_____

_____

At the end of the activity

State the three most important discoveries learned from the activity along with the significance of each and how each can be applied.

1. _____

_____

_____

_____

_____

2. _____

_____

_____

_____

_____

3. _____

_____

_____

_____

_____

Instructor Feedback

Strengths:

Areas for Improvement:

Insights:

Name _____

Team _____

Date _____

Activity _____

Recorder's Report

1 Before the activity

Record the basic agenda or plan as outlined by the team leader: _____

_____

_____

_____

_____

_____

2 During the activity

Important information to be documented: _____

_____

_____

_____

_____

_____

_____

_____

_____

_____

_____

_____

_____

_____

_____

_____

_____

_____

_____

_____

continued on other side

During the activity

Important information to be referenced. Where did you get key information? _____

_____

_____

_____

_____

_____

_____

At the end of the activity

State the three most important discoveries learned from the activity along with the significance of each and how each can be applied.

1. _____

_____

_____

_____

_____

_____

2. _____

_____

_____

_____

_____

_____

3. _____

_____

_____

_____

_____

_____

_____

Instructor Feedback

Strengths:

Areas for Improvement:

Insights:

Name	Charles
Team	Team #4
Date	Jan. 13
Activity	The Terminology of Information Technology

Recorder's Report

1 Before the activity

Record the basic agenda or plan as outlined by the team leader: Our team will be creating a class glossary of information technology terms. There are 4 of us in the team, so we will split the Vocabulary list of 60 words evenly among the 4 of us. Each person will use the suggested resources (dictionary and the internet to find definitions. We will each use MS Word and create a document so we can merge the lists into a single document. Everyone agreed to send me their lists by e-mail and I will be responsible for creating, saving, and printing the final document which I will bring to class.

2 During the activity

Important information to be documented: Each team member will create a Word document that lists his or her 15 words. Definitions for each term will be added below each term. The source of the definition should be included in parentheses after the definition.

continued on other side

During the activity

Important information to be referenced. Where did you get key information?   The activity lists a dictionary, and the internet as the resources we should use. As a team we have decided to try locating definitions first in a dictionary, then on the internet. We will only use the internet if we cannot find a definition in the dictionary. We will all note the resource where we found each definition in parentheses after the definition.

At the end of the activity

State the three most important discoveries learned from the activity along with the significance of each and how each can be applied.

1.   We learned that there is a lot more to most of these terms than we had thought. Every one of us ended up reading more than just definitions we found. So many of the terms do relate directly to other terms.

2.   We all also learned that even a dictionary published in the last year was "behind the times" with respect to some of the terms. Technology moves more quickly than the recording of that technology EXCEPT by or in that technology. This means that if you're using software, for example, the best place to find information about the software will be IN the software (the help menu or web-based information on the company web site).

3.   We learned that it is a good idea to double-check that everyone understands their individual assignments before the group splits up. Two team members looked up the same list of words! We did not make sure that everyone understood which words they were responsible for. From now on, when we do a similar activity where we split up for everyone to do their own part, each of us will announce his or her assignment out loud, to the whole group.

Instructor Feedback

Strengths:

Areas for Improvement:

Insights:

Name _____

Team _____

Date _____

Activity _____

Spokesperson's Report

1 Knowledge Level

Consider the knowledge level of the content you plan to present

Level 1 — stating facts, information, and discoveries

Level 2 — demonstrating comprehension (answering why)

Level 3 — applying knowledge (describing how)

Level 4 — analyzing and solving problems (generalizing)

2 Develop the structure of your report

Opening Statement:

_____

_____

_____

_____

_____

_____

_____

Main points which support or justify the opening statement:

_____

_____

_____

_____

_____

_____

_____

_____

Conclusions, recommendations, and/or applications:

_____

_____

_____

_____

_____

_____

_____

Instructor Feedback

Strengths:

Areas for Improvement:

Insights:

Spokesperson's Report

Name   Martin
Team   Freedom
Date   August 28, 1963
Activity   March on Washington

1 Knowledge Level

Consider the knowledge level of the content you plan to present

Level 1 — stating facts, information, and discoveries

Level 2 — demonstrating comprehension (answering why)

Level 3 — applying knowledge (describing how)

Level 4 — analyzing and solving problems (generalizing)

2 Develop the structure of your report

Opening Statement:

Five score years ago, a great American, in whose symbolic shadow we stand today, signed the Emancipation Proclamation. This momentous decree came as a great beacon light of hope to millions of Negro slaves who had been seared in the flames of withering injustice. It came as a joyous daybreak to end the long night of their captivity. But one hundred years later, the Negro still is not free.

Main points which support or justify the opening statement:

Citizenship rights must be extended to all Americans (Constitution & Declaration of Independence were a "promise that all men...would be guaranteed the unalienable rights"), shared destiny of the Negro community and white brothers ("their freedom is bound to our freedom"), "unspeakable horrors of police brutality" against Negroes must end, social mobility should not be "from a small ghetto to a larger one", signs stating "For Whites Only" 'strip our children of their selfhood and dignity', "a Negro in Mississippi cannot vote and a Negro in New York believes he has nothing for which to vote".

Conclusions, recommendations, and/or applications:

All should return to their homes, knowing that things must be changed and will be changed. Do not wallow in the valley of despair. When freedom is allowed to ring from every mountain top in America, from every village and hamlet, from every state and city, all black men and white men, Jews and Gentiles, Protestants and Catholics, will be able to join hands and sing in the words of the old Negro spiritual, "Free at last! Free at last! Thank God Almighty, we are free at last!" (We must continue to seek and insist upon equal rights for all Americans, regardless of race, color, creed, or religion. Civil rights must be the rights of ALL.)

Instructor Feedback

Strengths:

Areas for Improvement:

Insights:

Team Members _____

_____

_____

Date _____

Weekly Reflector's Report

1 *Team Productivity*

Our three greatest **accomplishments** or strengths this week were:

1. _____

_____

_____

2. _____

_____

_____

3. _____

_____

_____

Our three most important **areas for improvement** along with how we plan to make these improvements are:

1. _____

_____

_____

2. _____

_____

_____

3. _____

_____

_____

Our biggest challenge for completing our work effectively and in a timely manner was: _____

_____

_____

Our plan for overcoming this challenge is: _____

_____

_____

The most important resource we need to complete our work effectively and in a timely manner is: _____

_____

_____

continued on other side

Improved Team Performance

Compared to last week, our team has made improvements with respect to: _____

_____

_____

_____

_____

_____

Team Support of Individual Growth

Which team member(s) grew the most as a learner this week? Explain. _____

_____

_____

Which team member(s) contributed the most to the team's work this week? In what ways? _____

_____

_____

Team Dynamics

We had the most fun this week when we: _____

_____

_____

We worked most productively when we: _____

_____

_____

Our biggest conflict was: _____

_____

_____

We resolved the conflict by: _____

_____

_____

The most important teamwork issue we need to address in the future is: _____

_____

_____

Instructor Feedback

Strengths:

Areas for Improvement:

Insights:

Weekly Recorder's Report

1 Vocabulary

What were the most important vocabulary terms learned by the team this week? Explain the terms in your own words.

_____

_____

_____

_____

_____

_____

_____

_____

2 Resources

Identify the three most valuable resources used by the team this week:

1. _____

2. _____

3. _____

3 Knowledge Table

Build a Knowledge Table of the course for the past week.

Describe key **concepts** learned:

_____

_____

_____

_____

_____

_____

_____

Explain the **processes** developed or improved:

_____

_____

_____

_____

_____

_____

_____

continued on other side

Identify **tools** used: _____ Define **contexts** for application: _____

_____ _____
_____ _____
_____ _____
_____ _____
_____ _____
_____ _____
_____ _____

Discoveries

Identify your team's three greatest discoveries or understandings gained this week.

1. _____
_____
_____

2. _____
_____
_____

3. _____
_____
_____

Remaining Issues

What are your team's two most important questions to be answered or concerns to be addressed?

1. _____
_____
_____

2. _____
_____
_____

What concept, process, tool, or context does your team want to explore in greater detail? _____
_____
_____

Instructor Feedback

Strengths:

Areas for Improvement:

Insights:

Performance Improvement Tools

(Strengths, Improvements, Insights)

SII Self-Assessment Report

SII Performance Assessment Report

SII Team Assessment Report

Getting a Handle on Performance:
    The Performance Model

Performance Analysis and Assessment

Feel free to use this page for notes!

Name _____

Focus _____

Time period or activity _____

Self-Assessment

1 The following were my two greatest **strengths** along with the reasons **why** or **how** they were my strengths:

1. _____
   _____

2. _____
   _____

2 My two areas for **improvement**, followed by short and long-term **action plans** explaining **how** I plan to improve are:

1. _____
   _____

   Short-term plan _____
   (now) _____

   Long-term plan _____
   (in future) _____

2. _____
   _____

   Short-term plan _____
   (now) _____

   Long-term plan _____
   (in future) _____

3 An **assessment** of my performance against previous action plans indicates **progress** in the following areas:

_____

_____

My personal **growth** was most enhanced by doing: _____

_____

The reasons **why** I grew are: _____

_____

My mood and **attitude** toward learning during this time was: ___

_____

The most valuable **insight** I learned about myself is: _____

_____

Knowing this will **improve** my performance by: _____

_____

Instructor Feedback

Strengths:

Areas for Improvement:

Insights:

Name _____

Focus _____

Time period or activity _____

Self-Assessment

1 The following were my two greatest **strengths** along with the reasons **why** or **how** they were my strengths:

1. _____
_____

2. _____
_____

2 My two areas for **improvement**, followed by short and long-term **action plans** explaining **how** I plan to improve are:

1. _____
_____

Short-term plan _____
(now) _____

Long-term plan _____
(in future) _____

2. _____
_____

Short-term plan _____
(now) _____

Long-term plan _____
(in future) _____

3 An **assessment** of my performance against previous action plans indicates **progress** in the following areas:

_____
_____

My personal **growth** was most enhanced by doing: _____
_____

The reasons **why** I grew are: _____
_____

My mood and **attitude** toward learning during this time was: _____
_____

The most valuable **insight** I learned about myself is: _____
_____

Knowing this will **improve** my performance by: _____
_____

Instructor Feedback

Strengths:

Areas for Improvement:

Insights:

56

Name _____

Focus _____

Time period or activity _____

Self-Assessment

The following were my two greatest **strengths** along with the reasons **why** or **how** they were my strengths:

1. _____

_____

2. _____

_____

My two areas for **improvement**, followed by short and long-term **action plans** explaining **how** I plan to improve are:

1. _____

_____

Short-term plan _____
(now)
_____

Long-term plan _____
(in future)
_____

2. _____

_____

Short-term plan _____
(now)
_____

Long-term plan _____
(in future)
_____

An **assessment** of my performance against previous action plans indicates **progress** in the following areas:

_____

_____

My personal **growth** was most enhanced by doing: _____

_____

The reasons **why** I grew are: _____

_____

My mood and **attitude** toward learning during this time was: _____

_____

The most valuable **insight** I learned about myself is: _____

_____

Knowing this will **improve** my performance by: _____

_____

Instructor Feedback	Strengths:
	Areas for Improvement:
	Insights:

Name <u>Ashley</u>

Focus <u>my work</u>

Time period or activity <u>Writing a draft of an assigned paper</u>

Self-Assessment

The following were my two greatest **strengths** along with the reasons **why** or **how** they were my strengths:

1. <u>I was able to use a variety of resources to find information about my assigned topic which is helping me make my paper more interesting than it would be without such a variety of different sources..</u>

2. <u>I was able to create a draft of my paper well before the deadline, leaving me time to revise my introduction</u>

My two areas for **improvement**, followed by short and long-term **action plans** explaining **how** I plan to improve are:

1. <u>Transform my set of cited resources into the MLA format required for final submittal. Although we only had to turn in a draft list of sources, I didn't use the MLA format. I wasn't familiar with how to list sources that way.</u>

    Short-term plan <u>I will review the specifications of MLA for all the different types of resources that I have.</u>
    (now)

    Long-term plan <u>I will purchase a guide to MLA format so I can continue to expand my understanding of citing</u>
    (in future) <u>different types of resources.</u>

2. <u>Edit for word usage efficiency – tighten up size without losing any meaning My draft was too long, by a page. The paper is supposed to be 3 to 5 pages and my draft was 6.</u>

    Short-term plan <u>Through feedback by the instructor, I was able to see where there was redundancy in one whole</u>
    (now) <u>paragraph and I can synthesize two paragraphs.</u>

    Long-term plan <u>I will be more direct and active with language thus reducing non-efficient passive phrases</u>
    (in future)

An **assessment** of my performance against previous action plans indicates **progress** in the following areas:
<u>I am working more efficiently and am better able to search for information online. That helps a LOT by saving me time!</u>

My personal **growth** was most enhanced by doing: <u>By not just taking notes but carefully reading the information I feel like I really understand more and am more comfortable writing in my own voice *because* I understand.</u>

The reasons **why** I grew are: <u>I stopped trying to keep track of what other people said; I took notes but also thought about the cases they were making. I realized that writing a paper isn't just about writing; it's also about learning.</u>

My mood and **attitude** toward learning during this time was: <u>I started out feeling a bit overwhelmed but discovered that by working hard & worrying less, I was going to meet the deadline even while I was learning. That felt great!</u>

The most valuable **insight** I learned about myself is: <u>Once I understand something, I don't have to just repeat what others have said; I can explain it in my own words and in my own way. When I can do that, I KNOW I've learned something!</u>

Knowing this will **improve** my performance by: <u>Giving me the confidence to stop trying to memorize things and try to understand them instead. I may occasionally get something wrong, but I'm learning and thinking for myself.</u>

Instructor Feedback

Strengths:

Areas for Improvement:

Insights:

Name _____

Performance _____

Date _____

Performance Assessment

Performance Criteria

Performance criteria are standards of performance, clearly and explicitly defined, which allow both the performer and assessor to have a mutually understood set of expectations by which performance may be measured and assessed. Performance criteria provide simple-to-understand, realistic, and measurable values of excellence.

1. _____

_____

_____

2. _____

_____

_____

3. _____

_____

_____

Notes

In order to complete a high-quality assessment, it is critical that you closely and carefully observe aspects of the performance with special attention to how the performance meets the established performance criteria.

_____

_____

_____

_____

_____

_____

_____

_____

_____

_____

_____

_____

_____

_____

continued on other side

Strengths

Identify the ways in which a performance was of high quality and commendable. Each strength statement should address what was valuable in the performance, why this attribute is important, and how to reproduce this aspect of the performance.

1. _____

   _____

   _____

2. _____

   _____

   _____

3. _____

   _____

   _____

Areas for Improvement

Identify the changes that can be made in the future, between this assessment and the next assessment, that are likely to improve performance. Improvements should recognize the issues that caused any problems and mention how changes could be implemented to resolve these difficulties.

1. _____

   _____

   _____

2. _____

   _____

   _____

3. _____

   _____

Insights

Identify new and significant discoveries/understandings that were gained concerning the performance area; i.e., What did the assessor learn that others might benefit from hearing or knowing? Insights include why a discovery/new understanding is important or significant and how it can be applied to other situations.

_____

_____

_____

Instructor Feedback

Strengths:

Areas for Improvement:

Insights:

Name _____

Performance _____

Date _____

Performance
Assessment

1 Performance Criteria

Performance criteria are standards of performance, clearly and explicitly defined, which allow both the performer and assessor to have a mutually understood set of expectations by which performance may be measured and assessed. Performance criteria provide simple-to-understand, realistic, and measurable values of excellence.

1. _____

_____

_____

2. _____

_____

_____

3. _____

_____

_____

2 Notes

In order to complete a high-quality assessment, it is critical that you closely and carefully observe aspects of the performance with special attention to how the performance meets the established performance criteria.

_____
_____
_____
_____
_____
_____
_____
_____
_____
_____
_____
_____
_____

continued on other side

Strengths

Identify the ways in which a performance was of high quality and commendable. Each strength statement should address what was valuable in the performance, why this attribute is important, and how to reproduce this aspect of the performance.

1. _____

   _____

   _____

2. _____

   _____

   _____

3. _____

   _____

   _____

Areas for Improvement

Identify the changes that can be made in the future, between this assessment and the next assessment, that are likely to improve performance. Improvements should recognize the issues that caused any problems and mention how changes could be implemented to resolve these difficulties.

1. _____

   _____

   _____

2. _____

   _____

   _____

3. _____

   _____

Insights

Identify new and significant discoveries/understandings that were gained concerning the performance area; i.e., What did the assessor learn that others might benefit from hearing or knowing? Insights include why a discovery/new understanding is important or significant and how it can be applied to other situations.

_____

_____

_____

Instructor Feedback

Strengths:

Areas for Improvement:

Insights:

Performance Assessment

Name _____ Sam Bohn _____

Performance ___ Meghan's presentation on her chemistry research ___

Date _____ Oct. 15 _____

Performance Criteria

Performance criteria are standards of performance, clearly and explicitly defined, which allow both the performer and assessor to have a mutually understood set of expectations by which performance may be measured and assessed. Performance criteria provide simple-to-understand, realistic, and measurable values of excellence.

1. _Organization of presentation (how appropriate was it with respect to the audience and how complete was it — i.e., was it missing any critical elements?)_

2. _Quality of data presented (how scientifically sound were the methods used to obtain the data?)_

3. _Ability to answer questions from the audience (was an answer given and how accurate was that answer?)_

Notes

In order to complete a high-quality assessment, it is critical that you closely and carefully observe aspects of the performance with special attention to how the performance meets the established performance criteria.

Strong opening with good eye-contact. Slides used appropriately; slide #4 contained chemical formulas probably not explained thoroughly enough for audience, some look confused. Strong use of peer reviewed journal articles but probably pitched a bit beyond an undergraduate audience. Meghan is an interesting speaker & the audience wants to better understand. Lab experiences fully documented and written up nicely. This is high quality work! Question time: Meghan cited Study A when I think she meant Study D. That's a problem. Strong answers but rely too much on technical terminology that is frustrating listeners. Strong answer to question & interesting/provocative answer. Meghan doesn't seem comfortable with audience questions and seems to be a bit flustered. 5 questions asked, 3 very strong answers given, 1 incorrect answer (I think she simply misspoke but it is still incorrect), 1 question not answered. Is losing connection with audience. Gave a good 'next steps' conclusion. Audience gave polite applause; Meghan gracious in response.

continued on other side

Strengths

Identify the ways in which a performance was of high quality and commendable. Each strength statement should address what was valuable in the performance, why this attribute is important, and how to reproduce this aspect of the performance.

1. Organized: the presentation had all components, sequenced effectively for the audience, with appropriate pacing of content, and associated visuals.

2. Evidenced based: the presentation illustrated the methods used, experimental practices, data collected, and inferences based on sound data analysis with effective graphics

3. Interactivity: the presentation provided opportunity for audience to question and challenge the research, questions rephrased for understanding, and responses that addressed effectively questions or issues to produce greater understanding for all in the audience

Areas for Improvement

Identify the changes that can be made in the future, between this assessment and the next assessment, that are likely to improve performance. Improvements should recognize the issues that caused any problems and mention how changes could be implemented to resolve these difficulties.

1. Match the complexity of the presentation to your audience. The presentation was too complex for this audience. Provide definitions for the more technical terms and present conclusions without using disciplinary language that this non-technical audience didn't understand.

2. Maintain more composure when fielding questions. In listening to questions, take on their perspective, rephrase to gain understanding for what they are asking and then enter a teacher mode where you are helping them to learn and understand better.

3. Also related to the audience questions, consider rephrasing the question (checking perceptions) to make sure that the question that has been asked is the question you're answering. This will help your answers be as responsive as possible.

Insights

Identify new and significant discoveries/understandings that were gained concerning the performance area; i.e., What did the assessor learn that others might benefit from hearing or knowing? Insights include why a discovery/new understanding is important or significant and how it can be applied to other situations.

In assessing Meghan's performance, I was able to identify why I also have some trouble connecting with an audience. I become accustomed to using certain terms and need to be more sensitive to whether my audience has the context for those terms to be meaningful.

Instructor Feedback

Strengths:

Areas for Improvement:

Insights:

Name _____

Team Members _____

Date _____

Team Assessment

The following were our team's two greatest **strengths** along with the reasons **why** or **how** they were our strengths:

1. _____
_____
_____

2. _____
_____
_____

Our two areas for **improvement**, followed by short and long-term **action plans** explaining how we plan to improve are:

1. _____
_____

Short-term plan _____
(now) _____

Long-term plan _____
(in future) _____

2. _____
_____

Short-term plan _____
(now) _____

Long-term plan _____
(in future) _____

Our top three insights into working together as a team are (use the reverse of this form if necessary):

_____
_____
_____
_____
_____

Instructor Feedback

Strengths:

Areas for Improvement:

Insights:

Name _____

Team Members _____

Date _____

1 The following were our team's two greatest **strengths** along with the reasons **why** or **how** they were our strengths:

1. _____

_____

_____

2. _____

_____

_____

2 Our two areas for **improvement**, followed by short and long-term **action plans** explaining how we plan to improve are:

1. _____

_____

Short-term plan _____
(now)
_____

Long-term plan _____
(in future)

2. _____

_____

Short-term plan _____
(now)
_____

Long-term plan _____
(in future)

3 Our top three insights into working together as a team are (use the reverse of this form if necessary):

_____

_____

_____

_____

_____

Instructor Feedback

Strengths:

Areas for Improvement:

Insights:

Name _____

Team Members _____

Date _____

Team Assessment

1 The following were our team's two greatest **strengths** along with the reasons **why** or **how** they were our strengths:

1. _____
   _____
   _____

2. _____
   _____
   _____

2 Our two areas for **improvement**, followed by short and long-term **action plans** explaining how we plan to improve are:

1. _____
   _____

   Short-term plan _____
   (now) _____

   Long-term plan _____
   (in future) _____

2. _____
   _____

   Short-term plan _____
   (now) _____

   Long-term plan _____
   (in future) _____

3 Our top three insights into working together as a team are (use the reverse of this form if necessary):

_____
_____
_____
_____
_____
_____

Instructor Feedback

Strengths:

Areas for Improvement:

Insights:

Name _Robert_

Team Members _Robert, Laura, Terri, Julian_

Date _March 23_

The following were our team's two greatest **strengths** along with the reasons **why** or **how** they were our strengths:

1. We are able to compensate for one another. When Terri had a death in the family, Julian temporarily took over her tasks. When I had a major paper due, Laura was willing to hold the team meeting and give me notes afterward. Though it is best when we're all present, that isn't always possible. Being able to count on others really makes it easier.

2. Everyone on the team is great about communicating with the other team members. Though I'm the team captain, it is great that Julian set up an online chat room and EVERYONE participates. Everyone gets heard and we all seem to be comfortable sharing our thoughts and ideas. Not having to tip-toe around or worry about 'the quiet one' is nice.

Our two areas for **improvement**, followed by short and long-term **action plans** explaining how we plan to improve are:

1. Strengthen performance within roles. Casual use of roles, especially not using the forms very effectively has limited growth of team performance

   Short-term plan _(now)_ Will pair team roles so the pair member will assess the other's filled out form. Captain-Reflector and Recorder-Spokesperson.

   Long-term plan _(in future)_ Focus self-assessment on performing within a role. Use the performing in a team rubric to assess & analyze each performance to strengthen a very specific dimension of role performance during each activity.

2. Come to effective team consensus. During last activity, our team was split between two completely different responses and had to submit two different responses.

   Short-term plan _(now)_ Differentiate if responses are based upon values or opinions which justifies multiple responses, otherwise determine the critical inquiry question to clarify the issue separating the responses.

   Long-term plan _(in future)_ Long-term: Use compare and contrast learning skills better to see how the positions are similar and what is really different (once identified, have the Skeptic challenge premises and logic development)

Our top three insights into working together as a team are (use the reverse of this form if necessary):

I think we've all found that despite our moments of stress as a team, that working together means being able to do more than you can on your own. Having someone who is able to lend a hand when you're not able to do it all on your own is amazing and makes us all grateful that we have gotten to know each other. This is a VERY positive team experience which we ALL appreciate.

Instructor Feedback

Strengths:

Areas for Improvement:

Insights:

Getting a Handle on Performance:
The Performance Model

The Theory of Performance allows us to dissect a performance. Through this lens, we see that a performance is comprised of the following dimensions: identity, skills, knowledge, context, personal factors, and fixed factors. A performer has some control over all of these, with the exception of fixed factors.

IDENTITY
SKILLS
KNOWLEDGE
CONTEXT
PERSONAL FACTORS
+ FIXED FACTORS

= **PERFORMANCE**

Identity	As individuals mature in a discipline, they take on the shared identity of the professional community while elevating their own uniqueness. For a learner to perform well, he or she must have a strong identity as a member of a learning community. A student demonstrates identity as a learner when engaging in learning activities, such as attending classes and studying. A student who is performing in mathematics begins to demonstrate identity within that field by using the terminology of mathematics.
Learning Skills	Skills describe specific actions that are used by individuals, groups, or organizations in multiple types of performances. Within education, the focus is on those skills that are transferable across contexts and allow individuals to improve their mastery of subject matter. These are known as *learning skills*. Learners who perform well work to increase their mastery of learning skills.
Knowledge	Knowledge involves facts, information, concepts, theories, or principles acquired by a person or group through experience or education. You are learning about the Performance Model right now and are adding to your knowledge with every word you read.
Context	This component includes variables associated with the situation in which the individual or organization performs. Each time you perform as a learner, you do so within a specific context, which includes a number of variables. For example, your performance in a course has, as part of its context, the way you meet (in a classroom? online?), how long you meet as a group, and so on.
Personal Factors	This component includes variables associated with the personal situation of an individual. Your performance as an student depends a great deal upon your personal factors and the life situation you are in. Personal factors can present a significant challenge to performing well.
Fixed Factors	This component includes variables unique to an individual that cannot be altered. These are the only aspect of performance that cannot be altered and include items such as the first language you learned, color-blindness, etc. While your performance as a learner is certainly affected by fixed factors, it is a mistake to automatically assume that your performance is constrained by these factors.

Performance Analysis and Assessment
(based on the Performance Model)

Name _____ Date _____

Performance _____

| **Identity** | Describe the Identity: _____ |

How will awareness of **identity** help to improve the performance? _____
_____
_____

| **Learning Skills** | Describe the key Learning Skills: _____ |

How will improving these **skills** help to improve the performance? _____
_____
_____

| **Knowledge** | Describe the Knowledge: _____ |

How will increasing the level of **knowledge** help to improve the performance? _____
_____
_____

| **Context** | Describe the Context: _____ |

How will awareness of **context** help to improve the performance? _____
_____
_____

| **Personal Factors** | Describe the existing Personal Factors: _____ |

How might the **personal factors** be addressed in order to help improve the performance? _____
_____
_____

| **Fixed Factors** | Describe the Fixed Factors: _____ |

Can awareness of **fixed factors** help to improve the performance? How? _____
_____
_____

Performance Analysis and Assessment

(based on the Performance Model)

Name _____ Date _____

Performance _____

| Identity | *Describe the Identity:* _____ |

*How will awareness of **identity** help to improve the performance?* _____

_____

_____

| Learning Skills | *Describe the key Learning Skills:* _____ |

*How will improving these **skills** help to improve the performance?* _____

_____

_____

| Knowledge | *Describe the Knowledge:* _____ |

*How will increasing the level of **knowledge** help to improve the performance?* _____

_____

_____

| Context | *Describe the Context:* _____ |

*How will awareness of **context** help to improve the performance?* _____

_____

_____

| Personal Factors | *Describe the existing Personal Factors:* _____ |

*How might the **personal factors** be addressed in order to help improve the performance?* _____

_____

_____

| Fixed Factors | *Describe the Fixed Factors:* _____ |

*Can awareness of **fixed factors** help to improve the performance? How?* _____

_____

_____

Performance Analysis and Assessment
(based on the Performance Model)

Name __Breanna Apple__   Date __October 16__

Performance __Writing a first literary work for publication: The Sorcerer's Stone__

Identity

Describe the Identity: __J.K. Rowling, though comfortable with the act of writing did not identify herself as a writer; she trained to be a teacher.__

*How will awareness of **identity** help improve the performance?* __In identifying as an author or writer, one generally has access to the support of other writers.__

Learning Skills

Describe the key Learning Skills: __imagining, making connections, producing humor__

*How will improving these **skills** help improve the performance?* __The writing integrates complexity with simplicity of creating (by imagining) new context and images that tie together. She consistently produces humor to contrast tension.__

Knowledge

Describe the Knowledge: __Rowling did a lot of research about wizards and magic, even using Latin in naming fictional plants and spells.__

*How will increasing the level of **knowledge** help improve the performance?* __According to Rowling, her mother died while she was writing the first book. She felt such loss and sadness and put that in the book as Harry's loss. Increased knowledge allows authors to make believable characters.__

Context

Describe the Context: __Most of Rowling's writing was done in cafes in Edinburgh. She wrote her manuscript using an old manual typewriter.__

*How will awareness of **context** help improve the performance?* __Knowing her context, she was able to plan how to use the time and resources she had available most efficiently. Rather than waiting until she could afford a computer, she used what she had and got the work done.__

Personal Factors

Describe the existing Personal Factors: __Rowling was a newly single mother, with a baby, who was surviving on welfare & going to school nearly full-time.__

*How might the **personal factors** be addressed in order to help improve the performance?* __Her personal factors contributed to the book taking longer to finish. Perhaps there were some alternatives? Daycare? A helpful relative? She did a good job balancing everything & just kept writing.__

Fixed Factors

Describe the Fixed Factors: __No known fixed factors.__

*Can awareness of **fixed factors** help improve the performance? How?* __If you are aware of your fixed factors, you can take them into account and find ways to work around them. If she had had no hands, for instance, she could have dictated the story and paid someone else to type it.__

72   Student Success Toolbox

Course Tools

How to be an "A" Student

Course Record Sheet

Beginning: Learning Contract

                Analyzing a Course Syllabus (Activity)

Mid-Term: Mid-Term Assessment

Closure: The Self-Growth Paper

                Course Assessment

Classification of Learning Skills

How to be an "A" Student

1. **Clarify shared expectations in the course**

   Ask, "What is expected of me?" and "What do I expect of myself?" (Tool: *Analyzing a Course Syllabus Activity*)

2. **Create a plan of action**

   Determine how you will meet the course expectations. (Tool: *Analyzing a Course Syllabus Activity*)

3. **Make your commitment to success in writing**

   Share it with another person. (Tool: *Learning Contract*)

4. **Prepare for class by reading for learning**

   Don't just read; read and think and ask questions. (Tool: *Reading Log* or notes with inquiry questions)

5. **Think critically in class**

   Ask or write down inquiry questions, connecting what you are learning to what you already know. Follow up on any questions that remain once class is over. Find the answers to your questions.

6. **Teach someone else**

   Pass along your learning to someone else as a way to test your understanding.

7. **Demonstrate your learning and increased understanding before the next class meeting**

   Use it or lose it. Find ways to use what you have learned.

8. **Extend your knowledge**

   Create a new problem to solve or try applying your learning in a new context.

9. **Anticipate future challenges so there are no surprises**

10. **Execute readiness preparation for every performance task**

    For a test, take a practice test; for an essay, write a draft. Find a way to practice or rehearse.

11. **Let go of your fear and stress**

    Finish your preparation for a performance such as a test not less than 24 hours before the performance. Studies have proven that relaxing and getting plenty of rest before performing yields better results than cramming or practicing up until the last minute.

12. **Engage in assessment and self-assessment after every performance**

    Regular assessment of your performance by both yourself and others will help you strengthen and improve your performance. (Tools: *Assessment Forms*)

Course Record Sheet

Course Name	Tests	Quizzes	Homework & Assignments

Course Record Sheet

Course Name	Tests	Quizzes	Homework & Assignments

Learning Contract

As a student in this course, I commit to:

1. Take risks

2. Work hard alone and with others

3. Take responsibility for my performance

4. Wanting and working to improve my performance

5. Fully participate in class

6. Prepare for every class

7. Be proactive, not passive

8. Be open to new situations

9. Be willing to assess performance

10. Not judge others' values

11. _____

12. _____

13. _____

14. _____

15. _____

Printed Name: _____

Signed: _____

Date: _____

Feel free to use this page for notes!

Activity: Analyzing a Course Syllabus

Learning skills: *clarifying expectations, inquiring, prioritizing*

Why

A well-written syllabus provides you with important information about a course including learning objectives, benefits to the student, content to be covered, important dates, and the basis for determining your grade. The syllabus involves an understood agreement between you and the instructor about what you will be expected to learn, the processes utilized to help you learn, and how you will be evaluated. By reading and analyzing the syllabus for a course, you know what to expect and where to concentrate your efforts to gain the most from that course.

Learning Objectives

1. Get a complete picture of this course including what your instructor expects from you.

2. Determine what you want from this course and how you are going to get it.

Performance Criteria

Criterion #1:   the inquiry questions produced concerning the syllabus

   Attributes:
   a. formulation of at least three questions
   b. the answers to the formulated questions cannot be found in the syllabus
   c. answers to the questions are relevant to this course and have significant value to other students

Criterion #2:   a plan of action for the course

   Attributes:
   a. includes clear obtainable goals to achieve from the course
   b. includes tasks and associated hourly efforts required to meet goals
   c. lists the top five priorities for success

Plan

1. Obtain a copy of the syllabus for this course.

2. Answer the Critical Thinking Questions.

3. Write three inquiry questions that you would like answered about this course.

4. After your instructor decides how to address these questions (either through an in-class or online discussion or a consulting session), record the answers to the questions.

5. Write a plan of action for how you will be a successful student in this course.

continued on other side

Critical Thinking Questions

1. What are the main sections of the syllabus?

2. List all the resources that you will use in this course.

3. What are the prerequisites (background knowledge, required skills, qualities, or attitudes) for this course?

4. Of the main topics covered in this course, which ones are of most interest to you? Why?

5. How will your grade be determined in this course?

6. What are the four most important things you believe a successful student must do to learn the most and to earn the best possible grade in this course?

-

-

-

-

continued on other side

Inquiry questions about the syllabus

_____

_____

_____

_____

_____

_____

_____

_____

Plan of action for the course

_____

_____

_____

_____

_____

_____

_____

_____

Mid-term Assessment

Name _____ Date _____

1. What are the three greatest strengths of the course? Why do you consider these strengths?

   -

   -

   -

2. What are three of the most important things you have learned related to your team and personal goals?

   -

   -

   -

3. What are three improvements that could be made to help you and others learn and perform better in the process of meeting your goals?

   -

   -

   -

4. What are three important topics that still need to be covered during this course?

   -

   -

   -

continued on other side

5. What have you learned about cooperative learning and teamwork, and how have you contributed to help others learn and grow?

6. What action plans can you and your team put in place that will help you meet your stated goals?

7. What have you learned about your own learning process?

8. Assess the effectiveness of this course in producing desired course outcomes.

Additional comments or questions you would like answered:

The Self-Growth Paper

Chances are that you have already had experience assessing your performance as a learner. How do you best demonstrate that your performance as a student and learner has grown? One approach is to complete a Self-Growth Paper. This activity is a unique and personal analysis and synthesis of the various self-assessments you have performed and improvements you have made throughout the course. As you prepare to continue your educational and life journey, you can consider this reflection paper as a kind of "map" or "travel itinerary." Where did you start this journey? Where are you now? Where would you like to go from here?

Your instructor and/or mentors have no doubt pointed out many of your strengths this semester and also suggested areas for improvement. These conversations and your own reflections and assessments have most likely led to your own increased appreciation for your strengths and areas where you can work to improve. Capturing these thoughts in a Self-Growth Paper will help you to appreciate how important it is to make action plans that reflect your new goals from one semester to the next.

While your instructor will determine the format, length, and other details for your Self-Growth Paper, it should focus on **five areas** that have been, are, and will continue to be significant for your ongoing and increasing success as both a student and learner. The following prompts should guide your analysis of your growth:

- In what areas did you face the greatest challenges?

- Where have you improved the most?

- What is one area in which you feel the most need for growth now?

If your instructor does not suggest areas for your focus, you should choose five learning skills from the Classification of Learning Skills.

The Continuum of Performance Levels (available on the following page) can be used to help you compare what your performance as a learner looked like *before* this course with what your performance looks like **now**. This is an excellent place to start.

Keep in mind that growth is not the same as learning. Knowledge is the result produced from learning. Growth is the result of personal development produced by self-assessment. In other words, you can learn a whole lot but still not improve your performance as a student. The Self-Growth Paper gives you an opportunity to look, not at what new facts and information you've absorbed this semester, but how you are now better able to learn in *any* class in the future.

Continuum of Performance Levels

	Knowledge	Social Interactions	Attitude	Abilities
Level 5 *Star Performers*	Can construct and modify models; are valued and respected by experts in the field	Create movements and organizations that often become self-perpetuating	Control their destiny and can control their emotions in challenging situations	Have highly developed learning and research abilities that enable them to excel
Level 4 *Self-Starters*	Are able to add to the knowledge in their discipline	Use relationships effectively to attain success for themselves and others	Seek greater challenges and responsibilities to perform at a higher level and push the boundaries of their own performance	Are able to cultivate new abilities in unfamiliar areas
Level 3 *Responsive Individuals*	Use their problem-solving, learning, and thinking skills to improve their performance and obtain higher-quality results	Are positive people whom others enjoy being around and want to have on their teams	React to challenges with improved performance rather than complaints, feeling good about their accomplishments	Are able to learn from how other people function in a particular area
Level 2 *Content Individuals*	Are satisfied with their modest levels of effort in gaining knowledge	Interact freely with family and friends, but do not seek more diverse contacts and more challenging relationships	Feel like a cog in the machinery, doing little more than what is asked, feeling their contributions are not very significant	Have enough critical thinking and analytic abilities to perform some degree of problem-solving
Level 1 *Static Individuals*	Try to minimize or avoid the effort needed to gain knowledge	Limit their social interactions to like-minded individuals who complain about what they are not getting out of life	Feel that whatever they do will have little impact, that most things are not worth the effort	Must have explicitly defined rules, procedures and policies; need to be prompted to finish something

Student Success Toolbox

Course Assessment

Name _____ Date _____

1. Review the Course Outcomes or Goals as presented in your course syllabus. Note each outcome/goal below and assess to what degree that outcome/goal was met.

   Outcome/Goal   **Degree to which it was met**

   _____   _____

   _____   _____

   _____   _____

   _____   _____

   _____   _____

   _____   _____

2. What are the three greatest strengths of the course? Why do you consider these strengths?

   •

   •

   •

3. What are three aspects of the course that you feel could be improved to help students meet course outcomes/goals?

   •

   •

   •

4. How do you plan to use what you have learned in this course?

   •

   •

   •

space for additional feedback is available on the reverse of this page

Additional feedback: _____

_____

_____

_____

_____

_____

_____

_____

_____

_____

_____

_____

_____

_____

_____

_____

_____

_____

_____

_____

_____

_____

Classification of Learning Skills

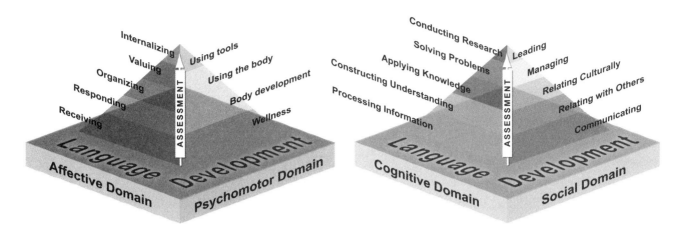

The Classification of Learning Skills for Educational Enrichment and Assessment (CLS) represents a 15-year research effort by a team of process educators who created this resource to assist with the holistic development of their students. Used by both faculty and students, the CLS is a valuable tool which helps to identify key processes and skills fundamental to learning. It also provides the framework for making quality assessments of performance and serves as a guide for improving assessment and self-assessment skills.

Faculty who teach using active learning formats will find this resource especially useful when measuring, assessing, and improving student performance. Students can use the CLS to identify the most important skills required to perform at the level of a skilled practitioner in various content areas.

What is a Learning Skill?

Learning skills are discrete entities that are embedded in everyday behavior and operate in conjunction with specialized knowledge. They can be consciously improved and refined. Once they are, the rate and effectiveness of overall learning increases. They can be identified at an early stage of a learner's development. No matter what a person's age or experience, learning skills can be improved, leading to higher levels of performance through self-assessment, self-discipline, or guidance by a mentor. This growth in learning skill development is usually triggered by a learning challenge of some kind and is facilitated by actions built on a shared language between mentor and mentee.

Development of the Classification

Initial work on The Classification of Learning Skills focused on the cognitive domain, looking primarily at critical thinking and problem solving skills. Benjamin Bloom's Taxonomy of Educational Objectives served as a resource during the construction of the cognitive domain. Efforts to build the social domain coincided with research projects such as the SCANS Report (*Secretary's Commission on Achieving Necessary Skills*), which pointed out the need to help students develop communication, teamwork, and management skills. Daniel Goleman's seminal work on emotional intelligence profoundly informed the work on the affective domain learning skills. The CLS was further expanded when levels for learner performance were identified and terms such as "enhanced learner" and "self-grower" were introduced. By continuing the dialog about the design, implementation, and measurement of general education courses, educators across the nation have aided in the continual refinement of the CLS.

COGNITIVE DOMAIN

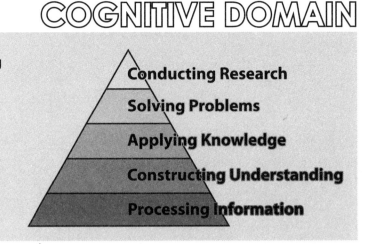

Processing Information

Collecting Data *(from a disorganized source)*
Observing, Listening*, Skimming, Memorizing, Recording Measuring

Generating Data *(to fill a void)*
Predicting, Estimating, Experimenting, Brainstorming

Organizing Data *(for future use)*
Filtering, Outlining, Categorizing, Systematizing

Retrieving Data *(from an organized source)*
Recognizing patterns, Searching, Recalling, Inventorying

Validating Information *(for value)*
Testing perceptions, Validating sources, Controlling errors,
Identifying inconsistency, Ensuring sufficiency

Constructing Understanding

Analyzing *(characterizing individual parts)*
Identifying similarities, Identifying differences, Identifying assumptions, Inquiring, Exploring context

Synthesizing *(creating from parts)*
Joining, Integrating, Summarizing, Contextualizing

Reasoning *(revealing meaning)*
Interpreting, Inferring, Deducing, Inducing, Abstracting

Validating Understanding *(for reliability)*
Ensuring compatibility, Thinking skeptically, Validating completeness, Bounding

Applying Knowledge

Performing with Knowledge *(in real context)*
Clarifying expectations, Strategizing, Using prior knowledge, Transferring

Modeling *(in abstract context)*
Analogizing, Exemplifying, Simplifying, Generalizing, Quantifying, Diagramming

Being Creative *(in new contexts)*
Challenging assumptions, Envisioning, Linear thinking, Divergent thinking, Transforming images, Lateral thinking

Validating Results *(for appropriateness)*
Complying, Benchmarking, Validating

Solving Problems*

Identifying the Problem *(to establish focus)*
Recognizing the problem, Defining the problem, Identifying stakeholders, Identifying issues, Identifying constraints

Structuring the Problem *(to direct action)*
Categorizing issues, Establishing requirements, Subdividing, Selecting tools

Creating Solutions *(for quality results)*
Reusing solutions, Implementing, Choosing alternatives, Harmonizing solutions

Improving Solutions *(for greater impact)*
Generalizing solutions, Ensuring robustness, Analyzing risks, Ensuring value

Conducting Research

Formulating Research Questions *(to guide inquiry)*
Locating relevant literature, Identifying missing knowledge, Stating research questions, Estimating research significance, Writing measurable outcomes

Obtaining Evidence *(to support research)*
Designing experiments, Selecting methods, Extracting results, Replicating results

Discovering *(to expand knowledge)*
Testing hypotheses, Reasoning with theory, Constructing theory, Creating tools

Validating Scholarship *(for meaningful contribution)*
Defending scholarship, Responding to review, Confirming prior work, Judging scholarship

Student Success Toolbox

Communicating

Receiving a Message
Attending, Reading body language, Responding, Checking perceptions

Preparing a Message*
Defining purpose, Knowing the audience, Organizing a message, Selecting word usage, Formatting a message, Illustrating

Delivering a Message
Selecting a venue, Generating presence, Sharing knowledge, Persuading, Storytelling, Managing transitions

Relating with Others

Inviting Interaction
Taking an interest in others, Initiating interaction, Hosting, Expressing positive nonverbal signals, Assisting others, Being non-judgmental

Relating for Meaning
Belonging, Befriending, Empathizing, Collaborating, Parenting, Mentoring

Performing in a Team*
Goal setting, Achieving consensus, Planning, Cooperating, Compromising

Performing in an Organization
Accepting responsibility, Being assertive, Making proposals, Documenting, Influencing decisions

Relating Culturally

Accepting Constraints
Obeying laws, Inhibiting impulses, Noticing social cues, Recognizing conventions

Living in Society
Sharing traditions, Supporting institutions, Valuing communities, Reacting to history, Being a citizen

Demonstrating Cultural Competence
Clarifying stereotypes, Appreciating cultural differences, Generalizing appropriately, Using culture-specific expertise

Managing

Managing People
Building consensus, Motivating, Modeling performance, Assessing performance, Evaluating performance

Building and Maintaining Teams
Defining team roles, Setting rules, Delegating authority, Confronting poor performance, Recruiting, Mediating

Managing Communication
Connecting with stakeholders, Networking, Marketing, Sustaining change

Managing Resources
Negotiating, Politicking, Securing resources, Creating productive environments

Leading

Envisioning
Projecting the future, Seeing implications, Balancing perspectives, Responding to change

Building a Following
Inspiring, Sharing a vision, Generating commitment, Maintaining integrity

Maintaining Commitment
Meeting individual needs, Taking meaningful stands, Thinking opportunistically, Being charismatic

Empowering
Giving credit, Encouraging ownership, Grooming subordinates, Being a servant leader

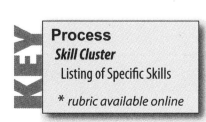

KEY

Process
Skill Cluster
Listing of Specific Skills

* *rubric available online*

Receiving (Being Open to Experience)

Exploring Self
Observing self, Listening to self, Perceiving reactions, Body awareness, Identifying emotions

Exploring Surroundings
Being curious, Being open, Being positive, Being playful, Being active

Experiencing Emotions
Feeling loved, Grieving, Feeling joyful, Laughing, Responding to aesthetics, Feeling secure

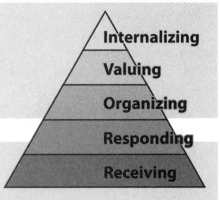

AFFECTIVE DOMAIN

Responding (Engaging in Life)

Emoting
Loving, Caring, Respecting, Giving, Comforting

Addressing Life's Changes
Coping, Persisting*, Accepting help, Believing in oneself, Responding to failure, Appreciating evaluation

Leveraging Life's Successes
Responding to success, Being humble, Seeking assessment, Celebrating, Acknowledging others

Organizing (Managing Oneself)

Regulating Self
Responding to requests, Recognizing dissonance, Managing dissonance, Managing resources, Prioritizing, Being self-disciplined

Managing Performance
Being decisive, Committing to the future, Preparing, Rehearsing, Challenging standards, Being self-efficacious, Orchestrating emotions

Managing Emotions
Modulating emotions, Recognizing emotional contexts, Preparing for future emotions, Modeling emotions

Valuing/Cultivating Values

Valuing Self
Building identity, Evolving a personal philosophy, Trusting self, Caring for self, Reflecting

Valuing Natural Laws
Appreciating diversity, Valuing nature, Valuing family/significant others, Being spiritual

Refining Personal Values
Identifying values, Exploring beliefs, Clarifying one's value system, Validating values, Aligning with social values, Accepting ownership

Internalizing

Synergizing Feelings
Associating feelings, Interpreting feelings, Analyzing feelings, Predicting feelings, Objectifying emotions, Exploring emotions

Facilitating Personal Development
Recognizing personal potential, Seeking assessment, Seeking mentoring, Being patient

Challenging Self
Exploring potential, Expanding identity, Being courageous, Being proactive, Growing culturally, Being empathic

Committing Beyond Self
Committing to caring, Accepting outcomes, Acting on beliefs, Enhancing self-esteem, Maturing, Self-actualizing

Stages of Learning Skill Development

Level 5 **Transformative Use**	The skill is expanded and integrated with other skills so that it can be applied in new contexts that inspire the emulation of others.
Level 4 **Self-reflective Use**	The skill can be self-improved and adapted to unfamiliar contexts with occasional advice from a mentor.
Level 3 **Consistent Performance**	The skill is routinely called upon and effectively applied in multiple contexts by the user, who consciously directs the effort.
Level 2 **Conscious Use**	The skill can be used proactively by a learner, but its use needs to be constantly encouraged and supported by a mentor.
Level 1 **Non-conscious Use**	The skill appears on a reactive basis in response to an immediate need, but without awareness of self or others.

Student Success Toolbox